MW00930932

BENNY

Nikki Husted

Benny

Copyright © 2024, Nikki Husted

This work, including its parts, is protected by copyright. Any use outside the narrow limits of copyright law without the consent of the copyright holder and the author is prohibited. This applies in particular to electronic or other reproduction, translation, distribution, and making the work publicly available.

ISBN: 979-8-218-37340-5

Author: Nikki Husted

Illustrator: Emily Crawford

For my sons. May you always feel peaceful, safe, and happy.

-Mommy

To my mom, for playing Pictionary with me.

-Emily

Every morning, when Benny looked out of her barn door, her heart filled with anxious thoughts. Her flock was bigger, faster, and a bit bossier. She was smaller, slower, and unsteady on her feet.

She was born with parts of her body in the wrong shape. Her neck was bent down and she couldn't move it the way other geese could.

Her wing flared out instead of lying flat on her side and it made it hard for her to keep balance.

She was scared,

anxious,

and unsure.

Instead of foraging around like the other members of the flock, Benny found a safe spot and waited patiently for the man to call, "babies!" because she knew this meant food would be coming.

7

However, the other flock members would push her around during feeding time. They used Benny's weakness against her and her self-confidence had faded to nothing.

The man noticed Benny's struggles and knew she would not be living her best life in this flock, so he found her another.

He was selfless,

kind,

and thoughtful.

That is the day Benny
came to live with us.

1

The lady who feeds us brought Benny down
to the barn. She used gentle hands and a soft
voice to help Benny eat and learn to swim.

Benny didn't look like us. She didn't smell like us. She didn't eat, walk, jump, or baaaa like us. We didn't care. We don't usually care about much other than food and whether or not the barn door stays open long enough for us to sneak out.

Benny joined our herd and that was that.

We were accepting, welcoming, and gentle.

14

We did have to learn to be careful around Benny. Her neck and wing made it hard to move fast so she couldn't get out of the way when we would run by. As hard as it was, we never stepped on Benny or pushed her away from her food.

At first, she was scared of us. But soon she grew so comfortable around us that she started following us everywhere we went. If we ran through the pasture, she shuffled after us. If we snuck out the barn door, she followed. She even slept near us in our barn.

We were buddies, friends, and together.

Even though Benny was fitting in with us goats, she missed being around other birds. After a while, the lady who cleans our barn brought us a baby goose.

17

The gosling, Jessie, stayed close to Benny. She was very frightened because she left the safety of her own flock to live with us. Many adult geese will peck at baby geese they aren't familiar with to show them who's boss; not Benny.

Benny showed the gosling how to swim and where to find food. She showed Jessie how to get in and out of the barn and where to sleep. She went looking for her when she made her little confused peeping noise.

She was tolerant,

patient,

and sympathetic.

It wasn't long before Benny and Jessie were the best of friends. They still lived with us but they waddled along together all day. Benny has even been seen sharing snacks with Jessie. She loved tossing them Jessie's way with her bill.

They call to each other when they are separated. Jessie
sits near Benny quietly while Benny lays her egg each day.
They sleep near each other in the shade of barn.

They are content,

inseparable,
and complete.

22

Benny is happy to spend her days in our pasture. She loves the rain, which we think is silly because we hide from it! She lays an egg in her nest almost every day now! Benny and Jessie swim in their pool, eat grass, and find earthworms together.

She isn't anxious anymore and doesn't get pushed around while she eats. Benny's confidence has grown a great deal. When we met her, she was anxious and uncertain of her place in this world. Not anymore.

She is peaceful, safe, and happy.

Benny is a real goose living in Ohio with the author Nikki Husted and her family. This is a true story about Benny's life.

Scan the QR code below to meet the real Benny!

The End

About the Author

Nikki Husted Is the author of Chicken Keeping Pure and Simple and runs the social media channels @purelychickens on TikTok, Instagram, Facebook and YouTube. She has her masters in Early Childhood Education but these days she finds herself educating others about chickens! She is a wife, mother to two boys, and has a whole crew of animals.

About the Illustrator

Emily Crawford is a historic preservationist and interior designer. She Is not a professional artist or illustrator, but when your sister-in-law asks you to be a part of something special — you accept. Emily lives in Ohio with her husband and two fur babies.

Printed in the USA
CPSIA information can be obtained
at www.ICGtesting.com
LVRC100930260424
778414LV00011B/129